Ready Steady Maths

Junior Infants Pupil's Book

Mary Hurley
Ber O'Sullivan

Instituid Oideachais Mhuire
COLÁISTE MHUIRE

Carroll
Heinemann

Contents

Early mathematical activities

Classifying 1-2, 4
Matching 5-6, 11-12
Comparing 3, 7-9
Ordering 10

Number

Comparing and ordering 55, 57, 89, 92
One / 1 16-19
Two / 2 24-29
Revisit 1–2 30
Three / 3 34-39
Revisit 1–3 40
Four / 4 46-50
Revisit 1–4 .... 51, 53-54
Five / 5 58-63
Revisit 1–5 .... 64-65, 71-72, 75, 84, 90-91, 93
Combining 81-83
Zero / 0 73-74

Algebra

Extending patterns 42-44, 85, 87

Shape and space

Spatial awareness 31
3-D shapes 41
2-D shapes 13-15, 32-33, 68-69, 77, 86

Measures

Length 20-23, 66
Weight 45
Capacity 56
Time 52
Money 67, 78

Data

Recognising and interpreting data ... 70, 76, 79-80, 88, 94

Sort

Colour

Sort

Colour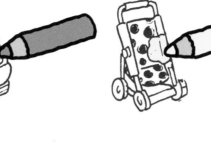

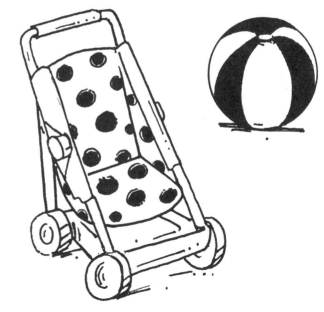

Big

Colour the big things

3

Sort

Colour

4

Match

Match

5

Match

Match

6

Bigger

Colour the bigger things

Smaller

Ring the smaller things

9

Match

Match and draw

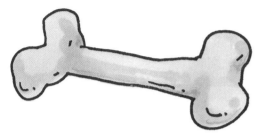

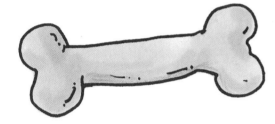

Match

Match and draw

Shape

Ring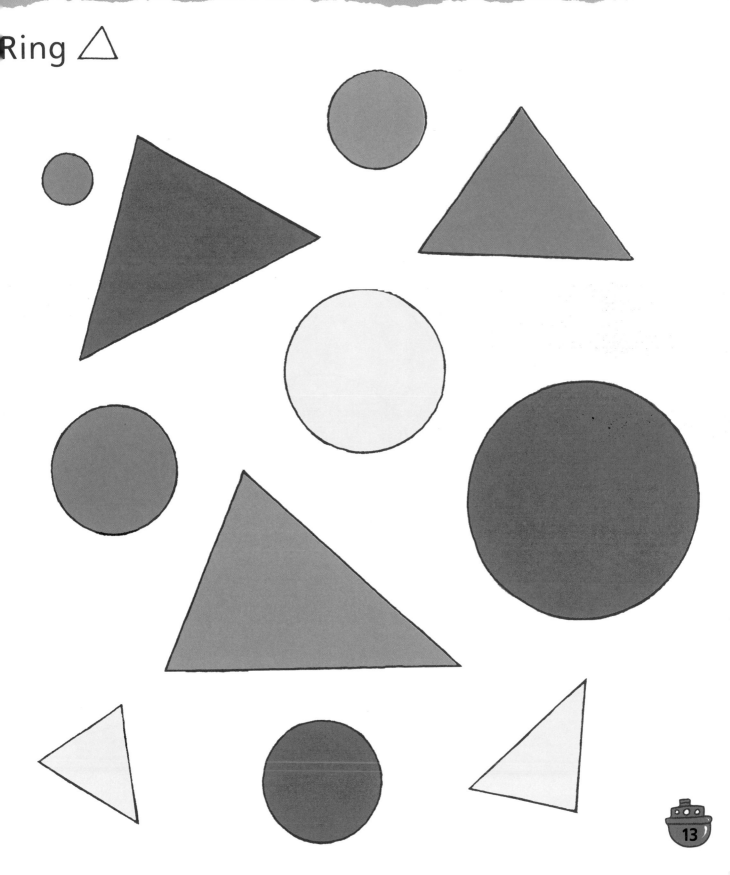

Shape

Colour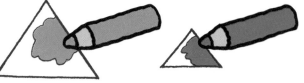

Shape

Colour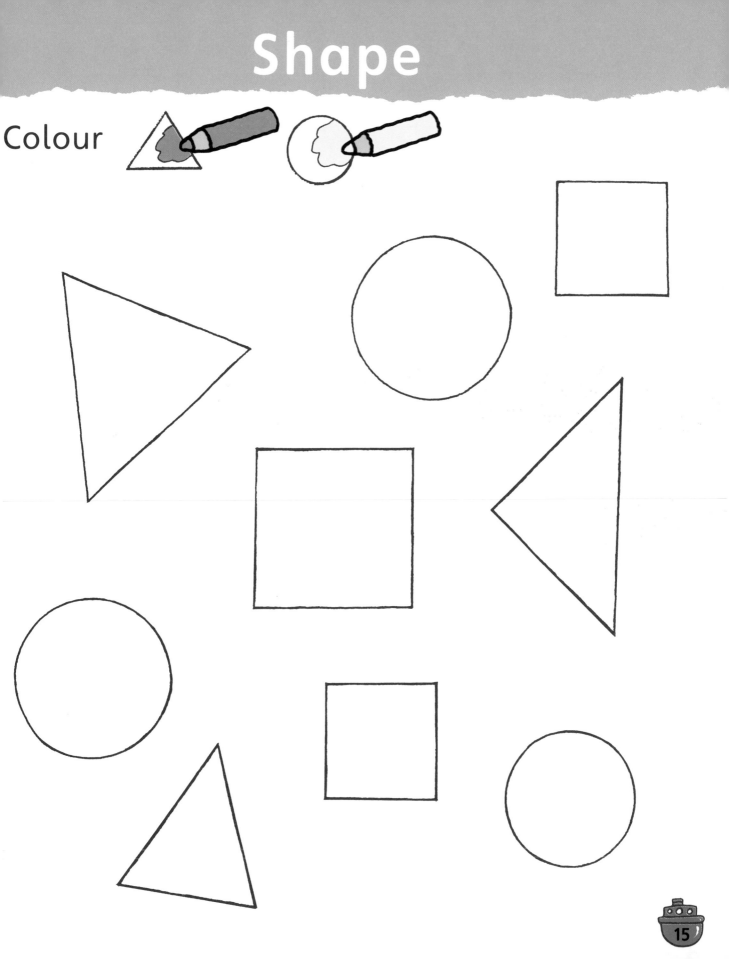

one   l

How many?

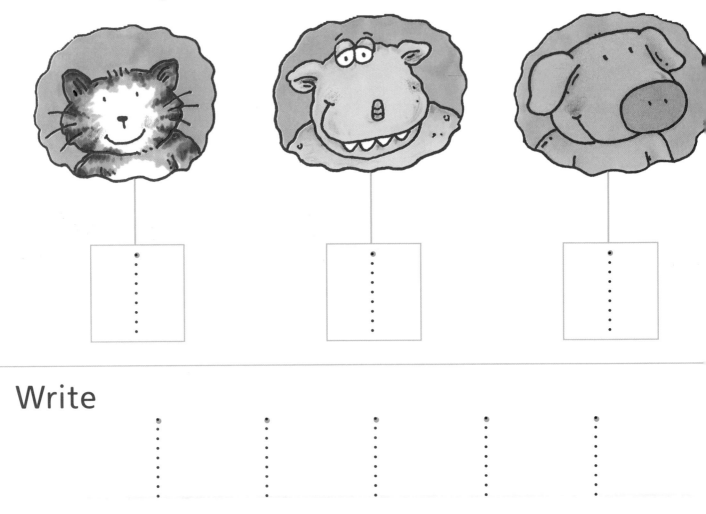

Write

Draw l

Colour 1

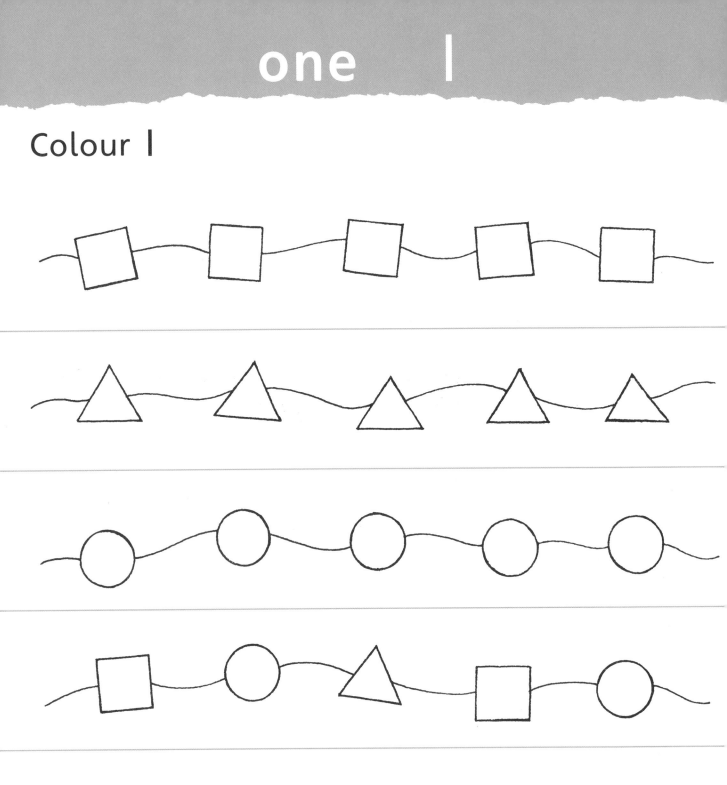

Ring sets of 1

19

Long

Colour the long things

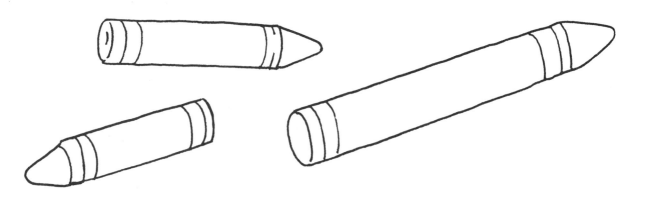

Short

Ring the short things

Longer

Draw a longer balloon

Long and short

Draw a shorter one

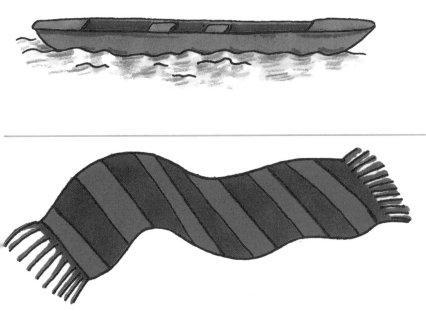

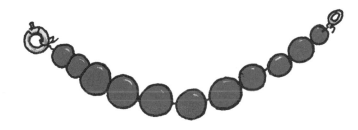

two 2

How many?

Write

two   2

1	2	3	4	5

Write

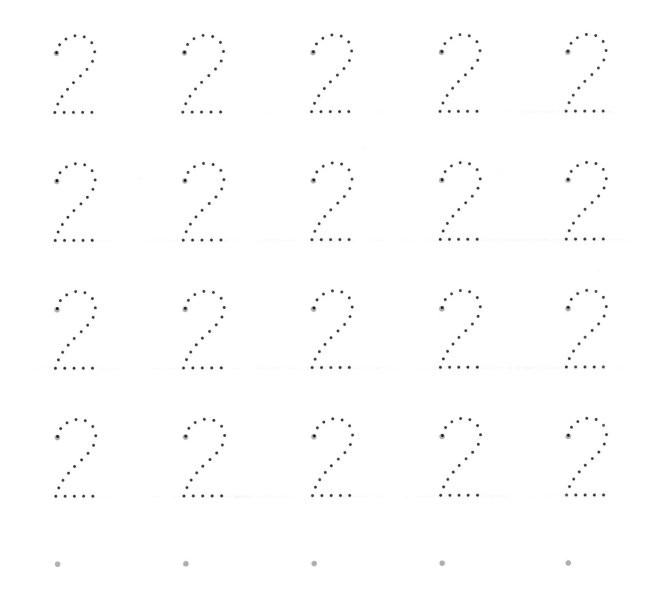

two   2

Write

Draw one more. How many?

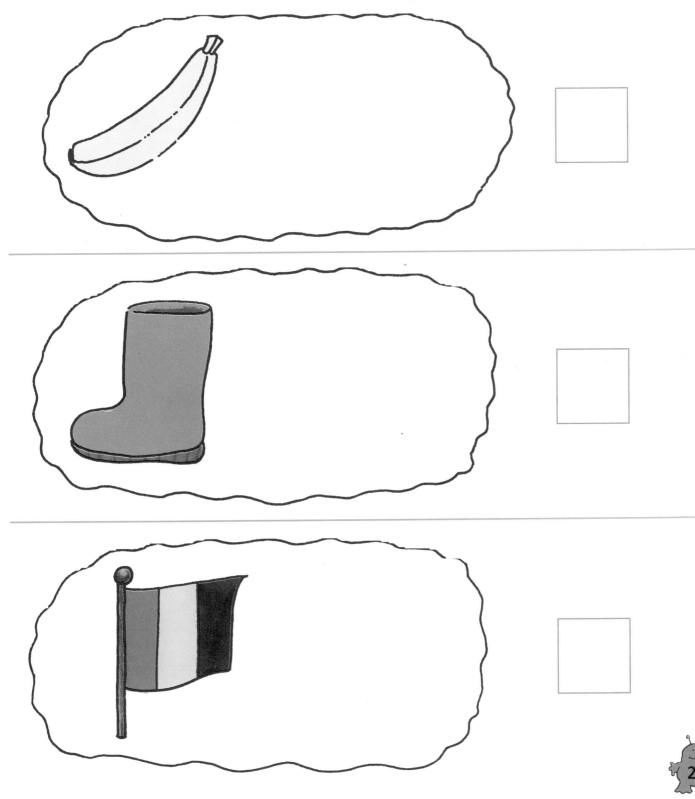

two   2

Draw 2

Draw 2

Draw 2

Draw 2

28

two   2

Ring sets of 2

How many?

How many?

2

30

Shape

Ring ☐

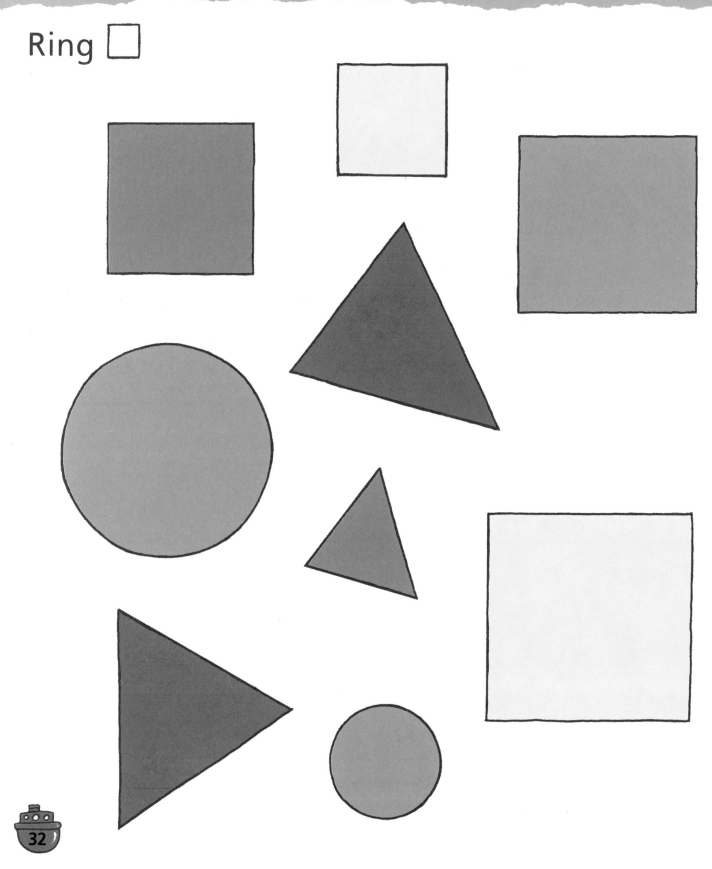

Shape

Colour

three   3

How many?

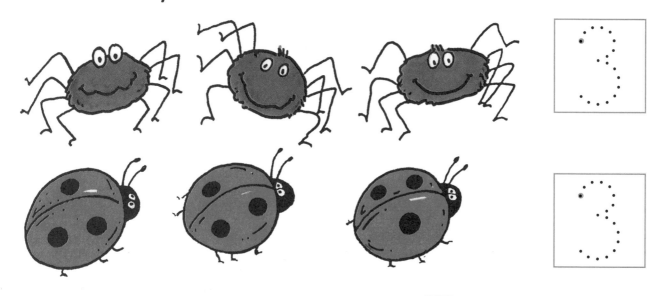

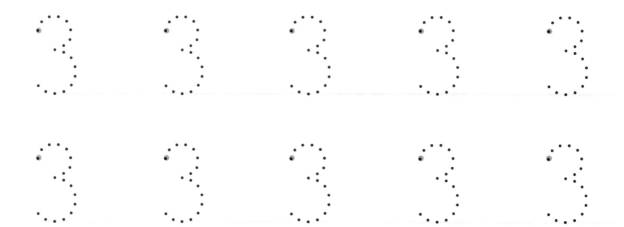

Write

34

three 3

| 1 | 2 | 3 | 4 | 5 |

Write

Write

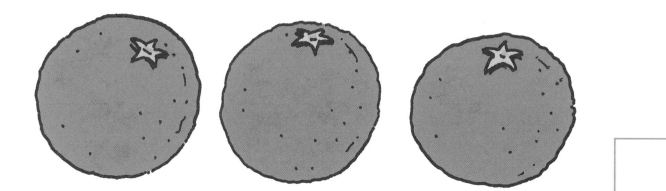

Draw one more. How many?

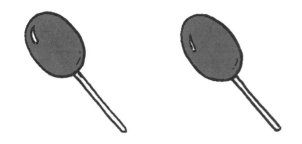

Draw 3

Draw 3

Draw 3

Draw 3

38

three   3

Ring sets of 3

39

How many?

How many?

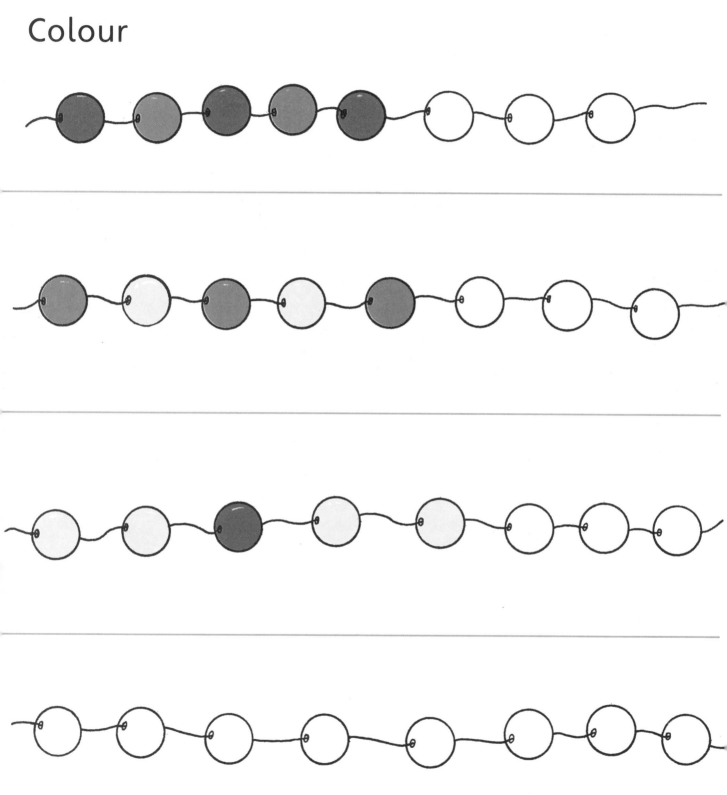

Pattern

Colour

42

Pattern

Colour

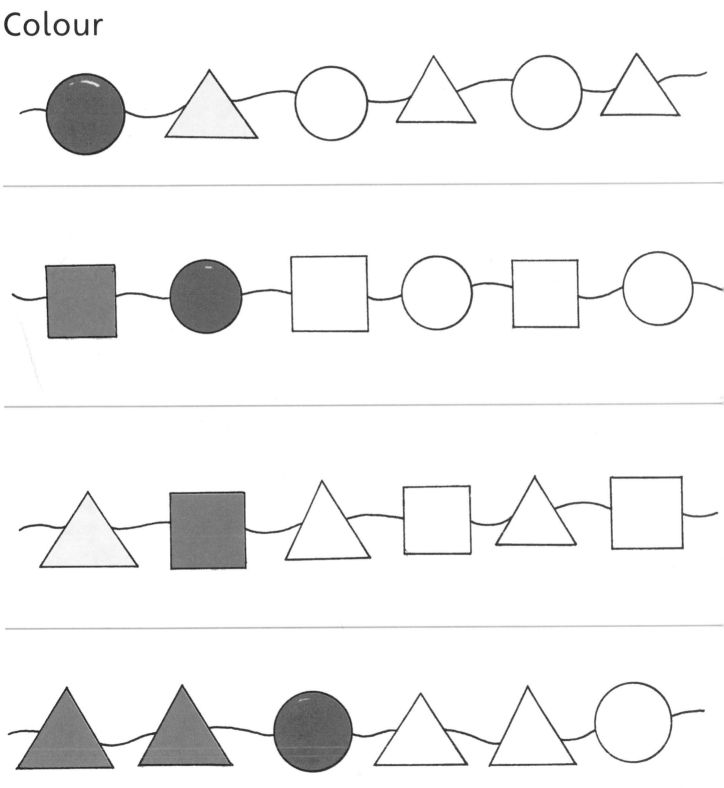

Heavy and light

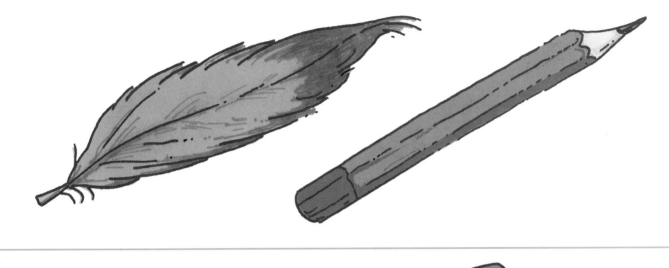

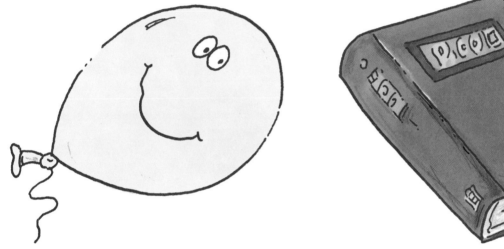

45

How many?

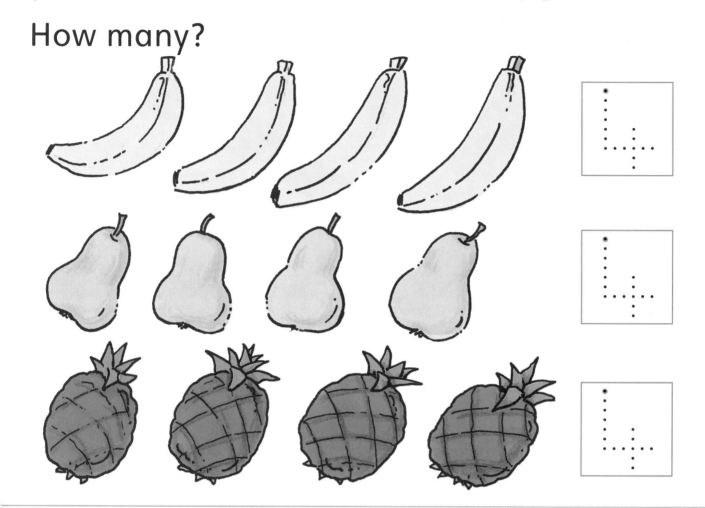

Write

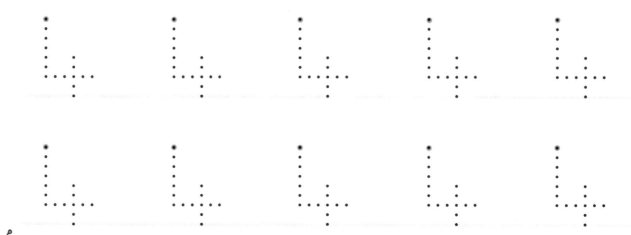

46

four 4

| 1 | 2 | 3 | 4 | 5 |

Write

four 4

Write

48

four 4

Ring sets of 4

Make 4

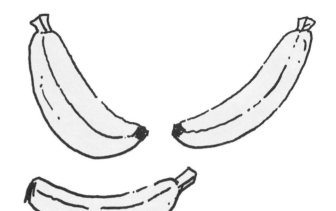

50

1 to 4

Colour 2

Colour 4

Colour 3

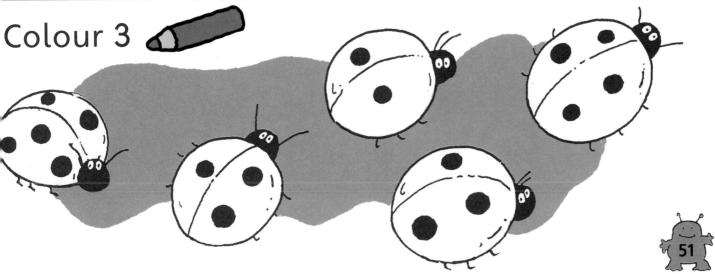

How many?

How many?

Match

 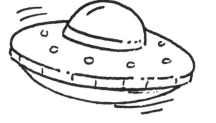

1

3

4

2

First and last

Colour the first

Colour the last

55

Full and empty

Ring the full one

Ring the empty one

First and last

Colour the last

Colour the first

Colour the last

five   5

How many?

Write

five 5

| 1 | 2 | 3 | 4 | 5 |

Write

Write

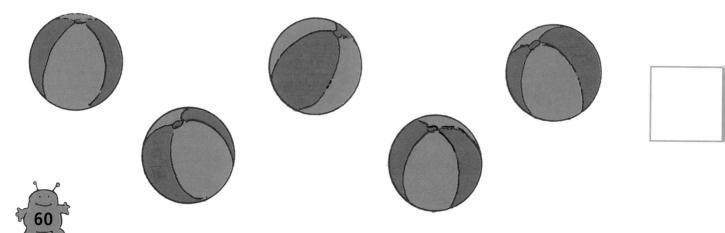

five   5

Draw one more. How many?

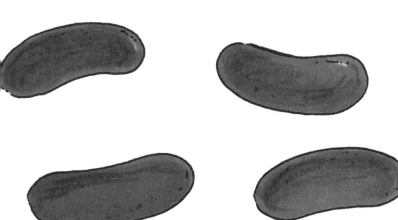

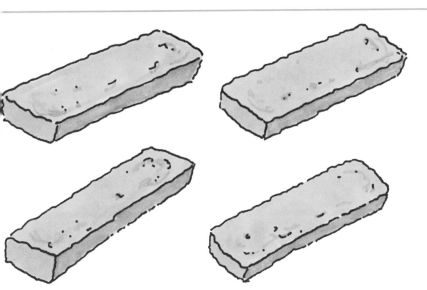

Ring sets of 5

Make 5

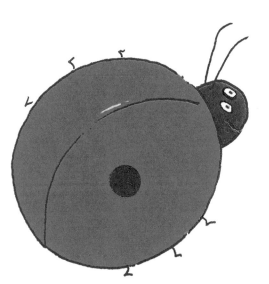
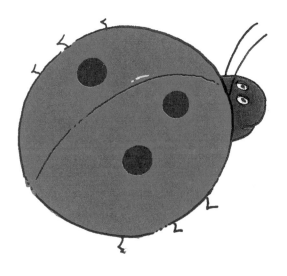
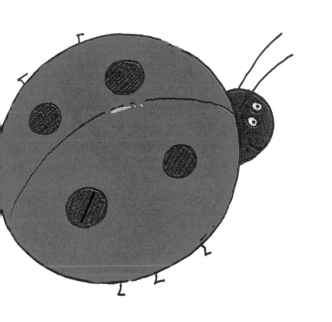
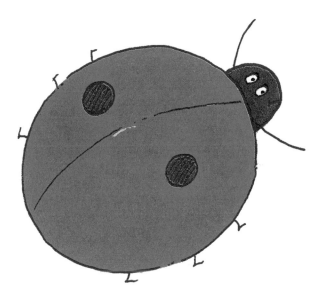

Colour

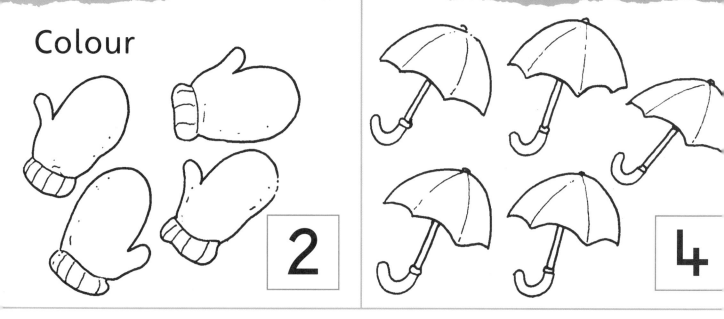

2

4

1

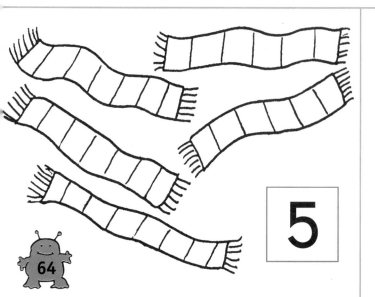

5

3

Draw

Narrow and wide

Money

Colour

Shape

Ring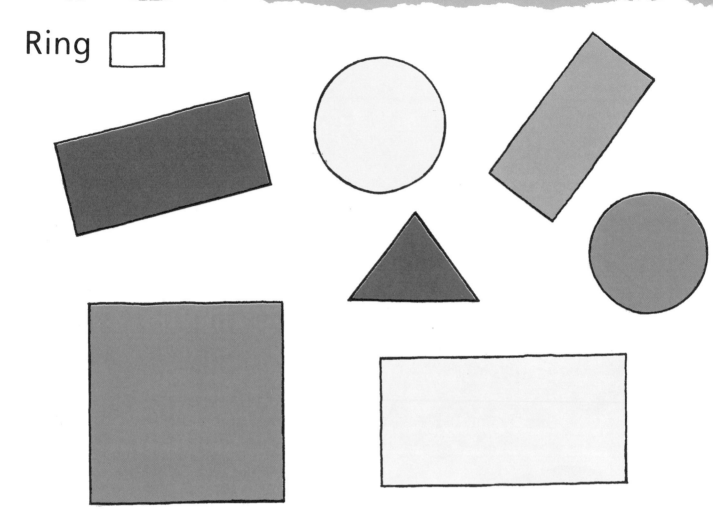

Draw

Shape

Colour

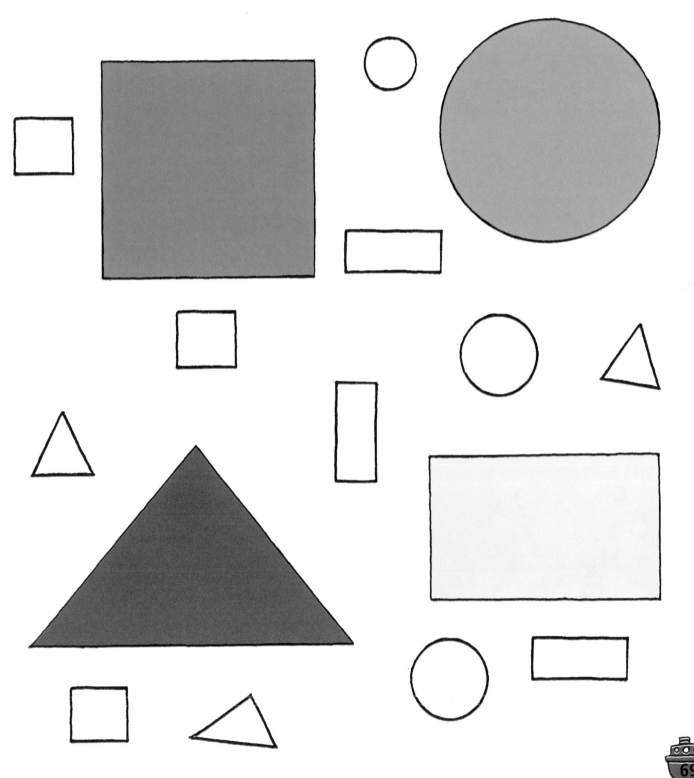

How many?

Colour

How many

How many

How many

How many?

How many?

Match

1

2

3

4

5

72

Empty set

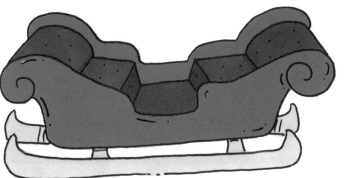

Zero

Ring the empty tanks

Write

How many?

How many?

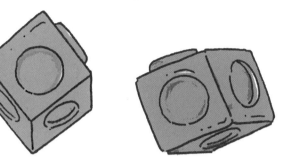

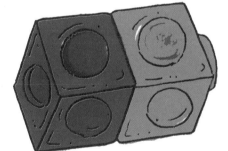

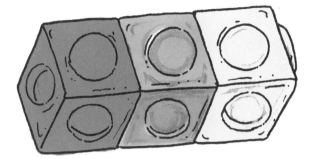

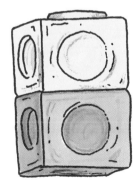

How tall? Use

Shape

How many?

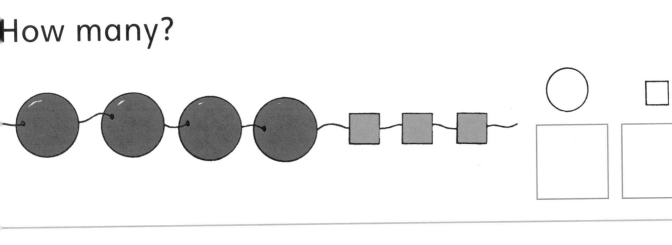

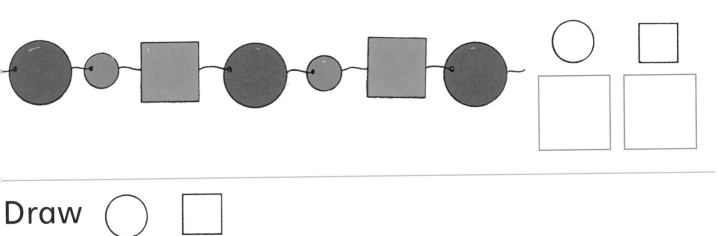

Draw ◯ ☐

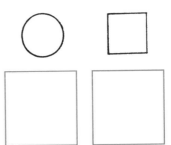

Money

Colour

Data

How many?

How many?

2 and 1 ➜ ☐

1 and 2 ➜ ☐

3 and 1 ➜ ☐

1 and 1 ➜ ☐

81

How many?

How many?

4   and   1   ➜   ☐

3   and   1   ➜   ☐

2   and   2   ➜   ☐

3   and   2   ➜   ☐

82

Make

Make

83

How many?

How many?

How many?

How many?

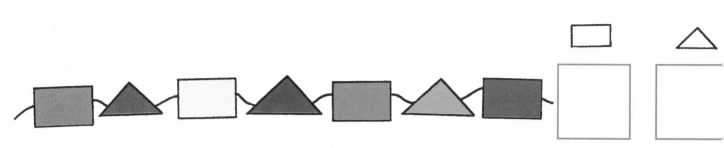

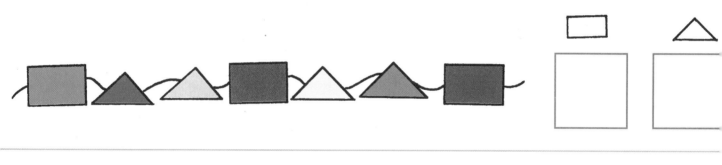

Draw

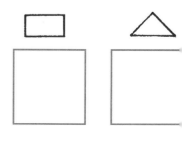

Pattern

Copy

Draw

How many?

How many?

Help the postman

Write the missing number

89

Countdown

Counting

Missing numbers

Write the missing numbers

Match

Match 🐻 to ⭕

Bug trail

Ring the bugs